Dr. Dee Dee Dynamo's

Satur... rise

By O...

Illust...

Dr. Dee Dee Dynamo's Saturn Surprise

PRT1114A
Printed in the United States
Library of Congress Control Number: 2014919384
ISBN-13: 9781620865569
ISBN-10: 1620865564
www.mascotbooks.com

To
The BROUSINS
Mark, Lucas and Jacob.
Your exuberance, intellect, youthful curiosity
and love for each other inspires me.
Don't ever change.

To
Our goddaughters, nieces, cousins, friends!
And
Smart and Sassy girls everywhere!

LEADERS OF TOMORROW.

OUR FUTURE LOOKS BRIGHT!

NOT EVEN THE SKY IS THE LIMIT!!!

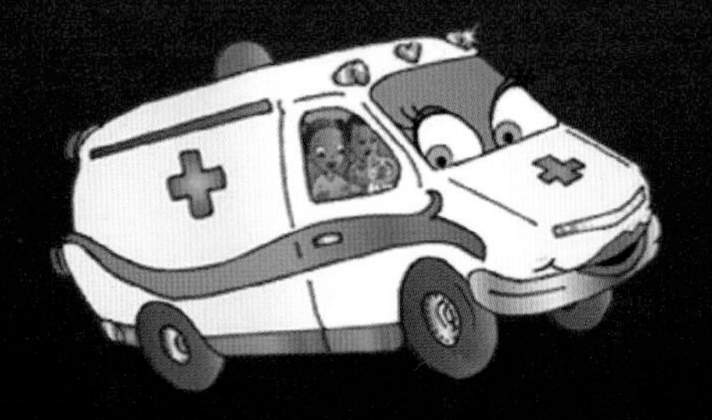

Dr. Dee Dee Dynamo bounds up the stairs of her favorite place, the Island of Positivity Planetarium. Lukas is hot on her heels. They can't wait to immerse themselves in the new exhibition.

Lukas heads straight for the star attraction: The Jupiter simulator called "The Battle of the Red Spot." Jupiter's Great Red Spot, a storm that's been raging for hundreds—maybe thousands—of years!

"Come on, Dr. Dee Dee, help me!" Lukas cries as he struggles to keep the ship stable in the hurricane-force winds.

As Dr. Dee Dee runs to join him—Buzz! Buzzzzzz! Her wrist vibrates and she looks down at Wyndee Watch. Wyndee's screen illuminates and Gordon the Gullible Globe appears, spinning and flashing his blue lights. Dr. Dee Dee turns up Wyndee's volume.

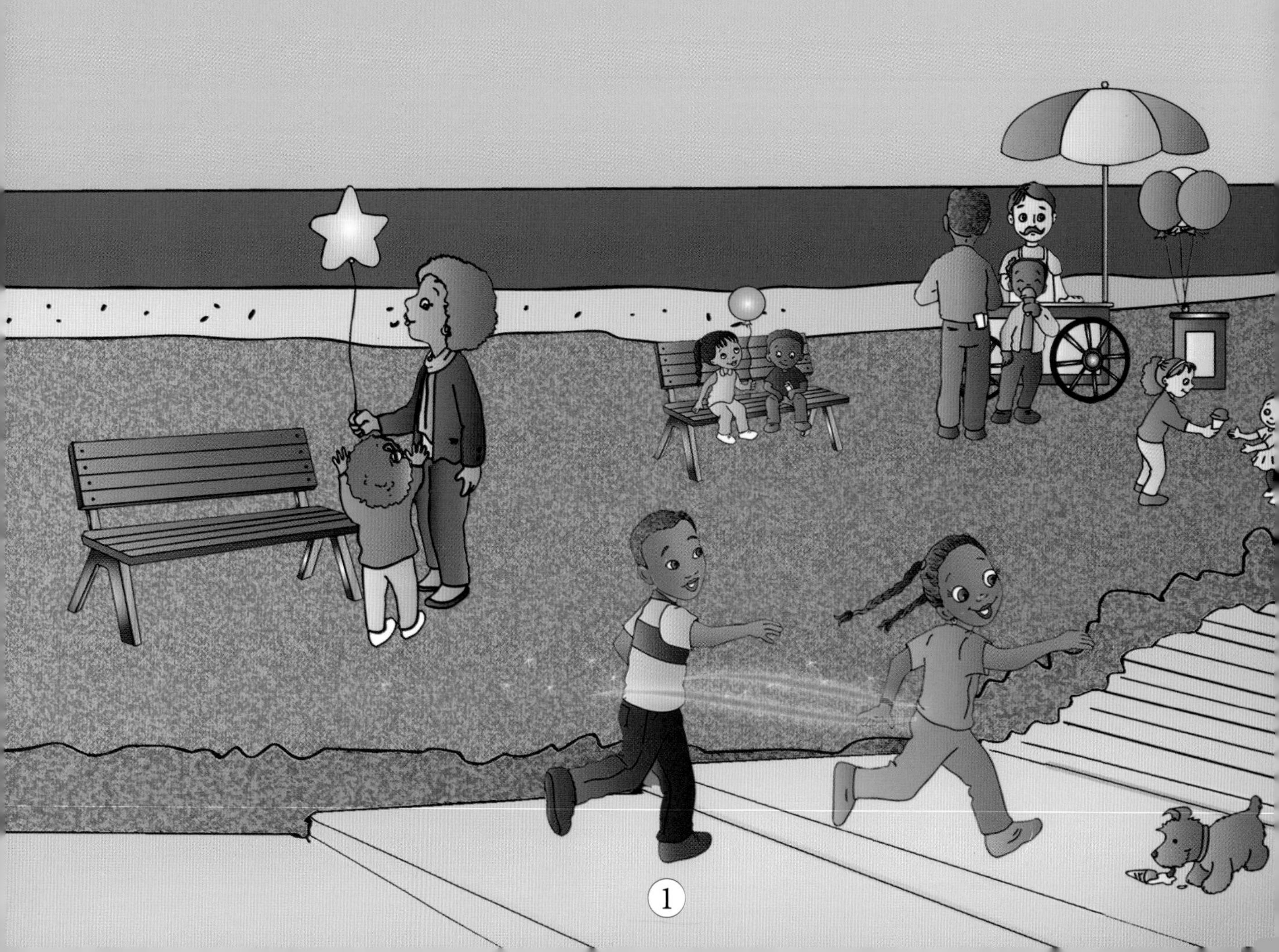

PLANETARIUM
OPENING DAY !!
RINGED PLANET EXHIBIT

WAHOO! WAHOO! WAHOO!

Gordon's alarm pierces the air, startling the other Planetarium goers.

"What is it, Gordon?" Dr. Dee Dee whispers.

"I heard sounds of pandemonium coming from Saturn—and when I looked out I saw that his rings were gone! Something is terribly wrong," says Gordon.

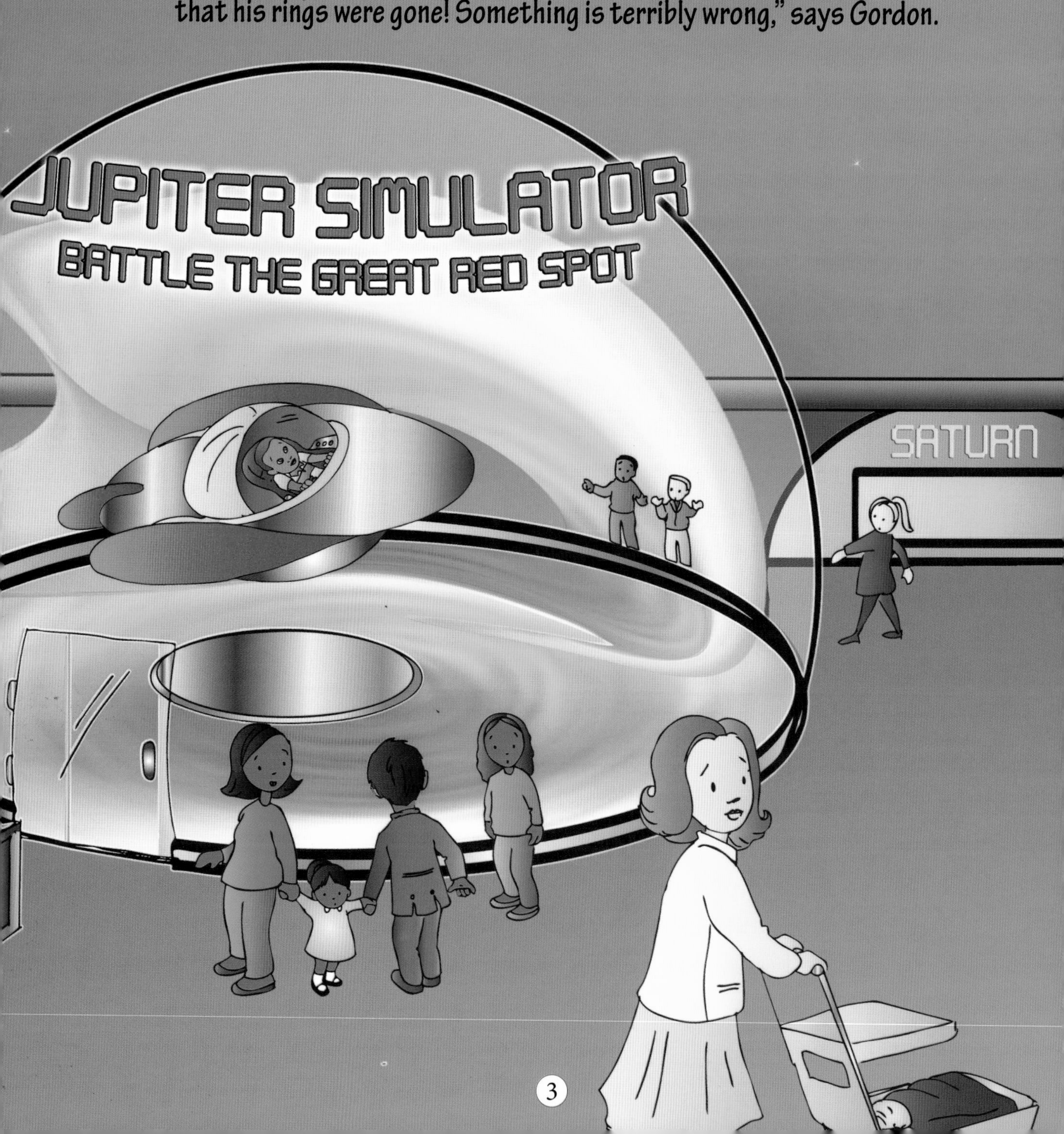

"Are you sure, Gordon?" asks Dr. Dee Dee. "There are times when we cannot see Saturn's rings from Earth, you know. When this happens, it is called 'ring plane crossing.' But the rings are still there."

"I'm sure, Dr. Dee Dee. We have to go!" Gordon insists.

"Sounds like we have a new mission," says Dr. Dee Dee thoughtfully. She pushes the alert button on Wyndee. It sends a shockwave signal to her team that it is time for another adventure.

She speaks into Wyndee. "Freeda and Kyle, please prepare the team and pick us up at the Planetarium."

Kyle's face appears on the screen. "This sounds like a wild goose chase, Dr. Dee Dee," he says. "Anyway, we can't leave. Have you forgotten that we are waiting for Uncle Beemore to arrive with our beehives?"

"Kyle, I also am super excited to meet the bees, but we need to check on Saturn," says Dr. Dee Dee. "Gordon is adamant that there is a HUGE problem."

Lukas is curious. "Why would Saturn lose its rings?" he asks.

"Well, ordinarily it wouldn't," Dr. Dee Dee explains. "However, every 14 to 15 years, Earth and Saturn line up in such a way that Saturn's rings are seen edge-on from Earth, which makes them invisible to us. That's the 'ring plane crossing' I was talking about."

"But if that's the case, I don't know why Gordon would have heard such a commotion coming from Saturn. Maybe something else is going on," Dr. Dee Dee wonders out loud.

"Maybe Saturn ate the rings!" Kyle chortles.

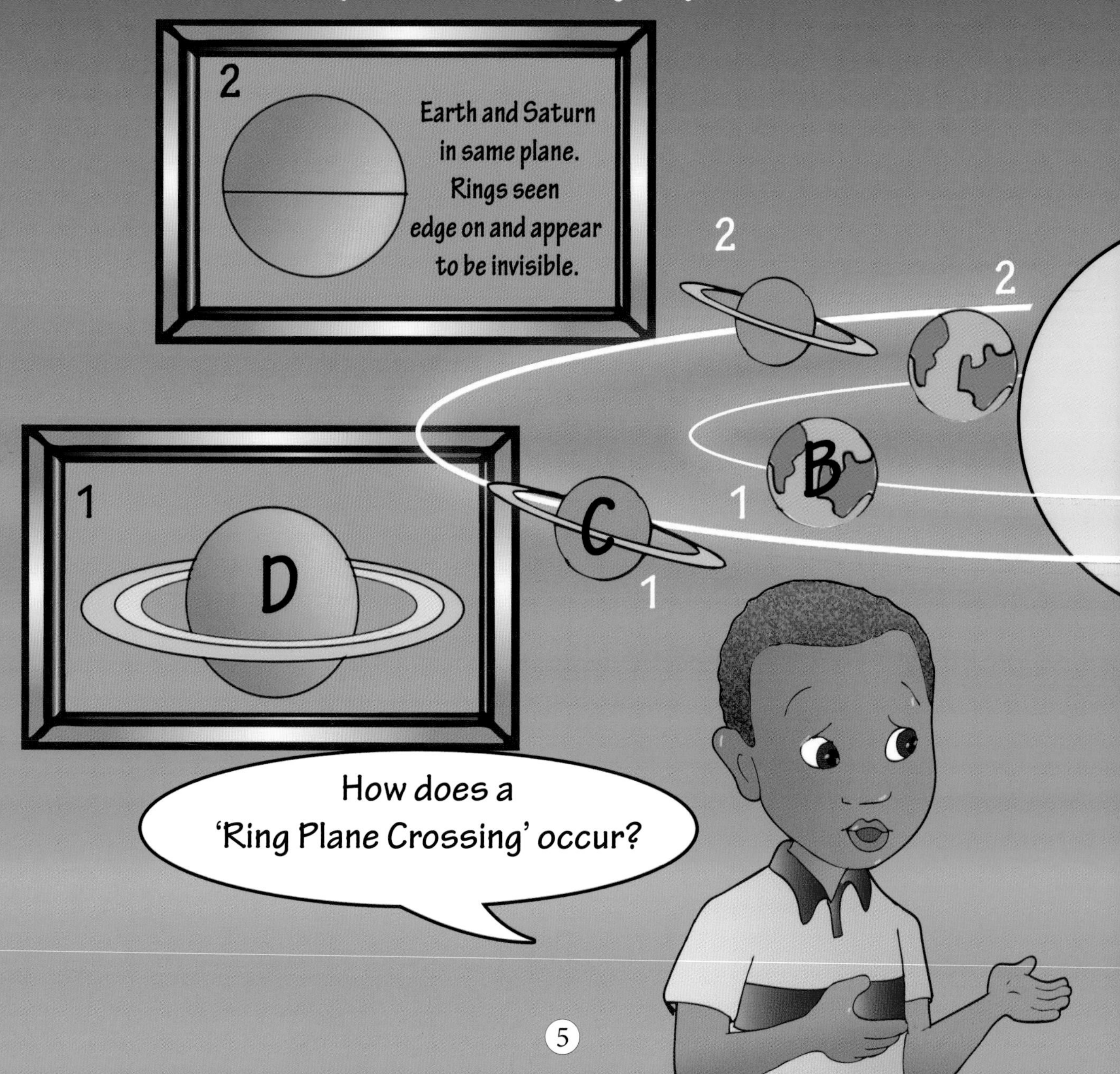

"Holymackarolee, Kyle! That sounds crazy!" says Lukas.

"It may not be as crazy as you think, Lukas," says Dr. Dee Dee. "Scientists have hypothesized that, billions of years from now, it is possible for Saturn's gravitational force to become so strong that it can pull the rings into the middle of the planet. After all, the rings are made of chunks of ice and rock."

Back at Dr. Dee Dee's workroom, Marky Medicine Bag opens and Ana Anesthetic, Sydnee Syringe, Slicey Scalpel, Nellie Needleholder, Suzy Suture, Raoul the Retractor and Simon Scissors jump in. They hastily follow Kyle onboard Freeda the Flying Ambulance and she launches into the air.

PLANETARIUM
Dr. Dee Dee Dynamo and Lukas jump
in as soon as Freeda touches down outside the Planetarium.
"Freeda, set GPS to Saturn and let's go!"

The Flying Ambulance makes a sudden turn sideways as they approach a very dark planet. Dr. Dee Dee almost falls out of her seat.

"Arriving at Uranus," Freeda announces.

"URANUS?" cries Kyle in disbelief. "Freeda, how could you have possibly forgotten so quickly that we are going to Saturn?"

"Oh, dear," says Freeda sheepishly. "I am so sorry. I mistakenly entered the letters S-A-U-U-R-N instead of S-A-T-U-R-N and the GPS rearranged it as U-R-A-N-U-S."

"Don't worry, Freeda, we all make mistakes," says Dr. Dee Dee reassuringly.

"Holymackarolee, this planet is spinning on its side!" Lukas observes.

Dr. Dee Dees whispers so as not to offend Uranus. "Poor Uranus. It must be so uncomfortable to live lying on your side. Let's help him."

"Dr. Dee Dee, please stay focused on Saturn. Uranus has been on its side for billions of years and doesn't seem bothered," Kyle states.

"Good point, Kyle," she agrees.

"Okay, Dr. Dee Dee," Freeda says confidently. "I have correctly entered S-A-T-U-R-N into the GPS."

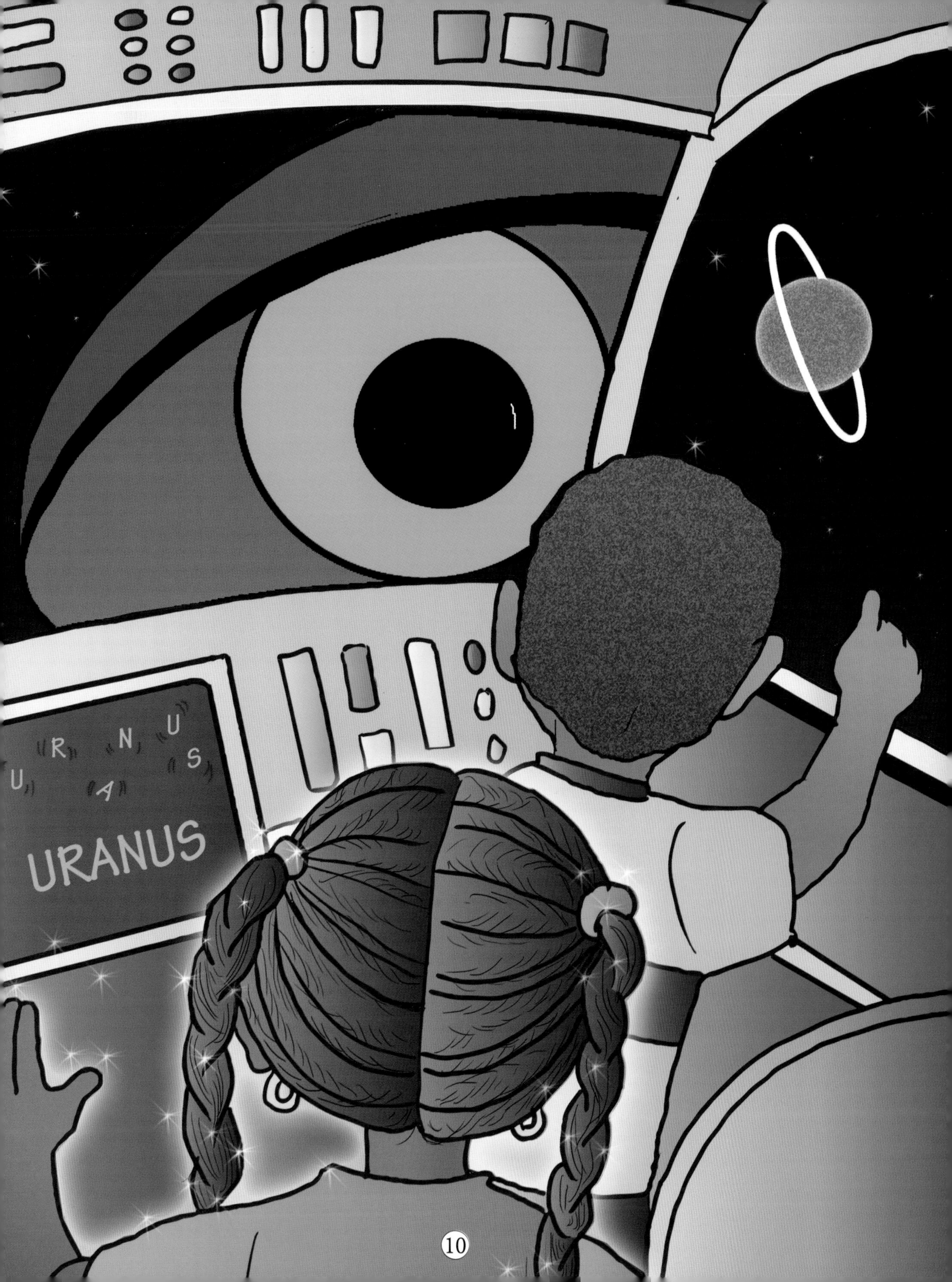

R N U
U A S
URANUS

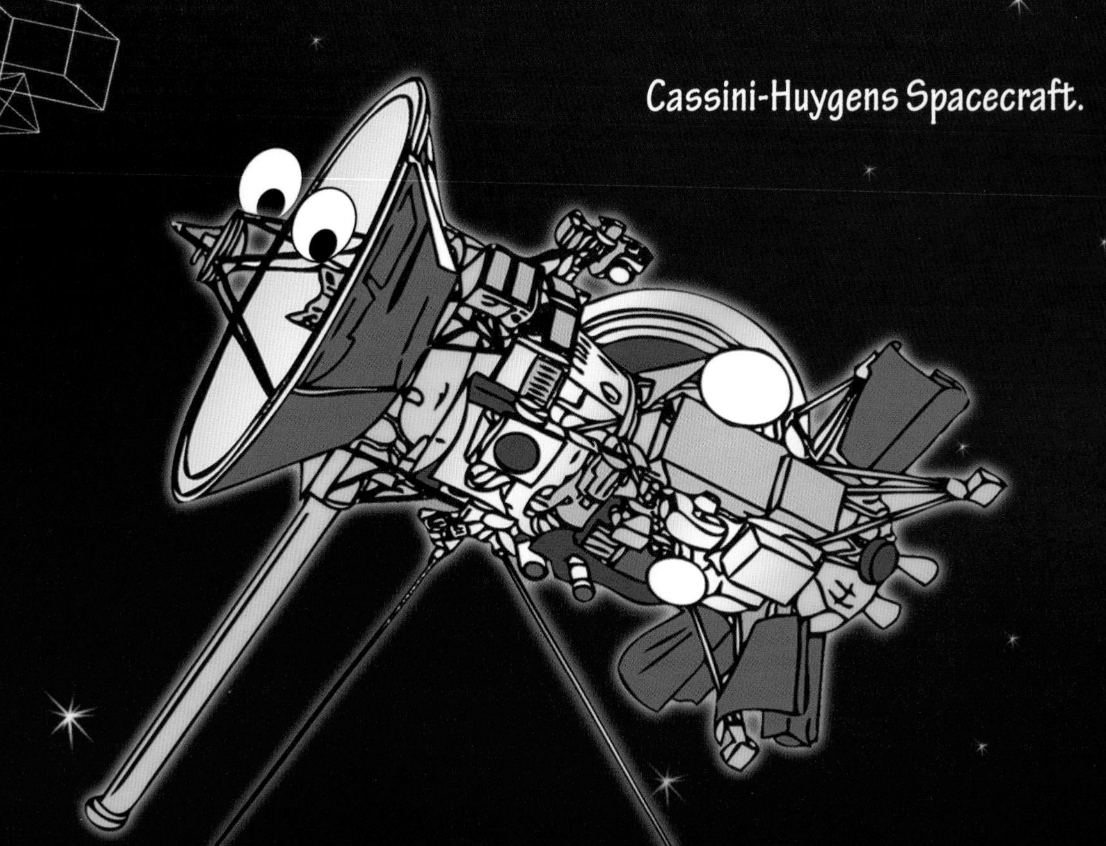

Cassini-Huygens Spacecraft.

As they approach, Saturn looks totally frazzled. There are fragments of ice and rock swirling everywhere.

“What now?” Saturn greets them in a tired voice. “Are you with the Cassini mission?”

“Who is Cassini?” asks Lukas.

Saturn explains, “The Cassini-Huygens spacecraft left Earth in 1997 and arrived here in 2004. It was sent by NASA to collect data and take photographs of me. They are focused on unlocking ALL my secrets. Now, I have no privacy. It’s very unnerving.”

“That would totally annoy me!” Kyle agrees. “I’ve heard about this. Didn’t they also discover seven more of your moons?”

Saturn grumbles, “If you say so. I don’t know how you discover something that has always been here.”

“Touché!” says Kyle.

Dr. Dee Dee introduces herself. "I'm Dr. Dee Dee Dynamo, Super Surgeon on the Go, and this is my team. My globe, Gordon, heard a commotion coming from this location and looked out and saw that you had no rings. I figured that it was because of the 'ring plane crossing' but I came anyway. However, I see you have BIG problems. This is truly a SURPRISE!"

"Oh, Dr. Dee Dee, Pluto talks about you all the time. You have to help me," pleads Saturn.
"My rings have gone *stark raving mad*. They don't want to be rings anymore."

"All of them?" asks Dr. Dee Dee.

"ALL OF THEM!" complains Saturn. "A, B, C, D, E, F and G!"

"Poor Saturn," says Marky Medicine Bag. "This looks like a disaster. What are we going to do, Dr. Dee Dee?"

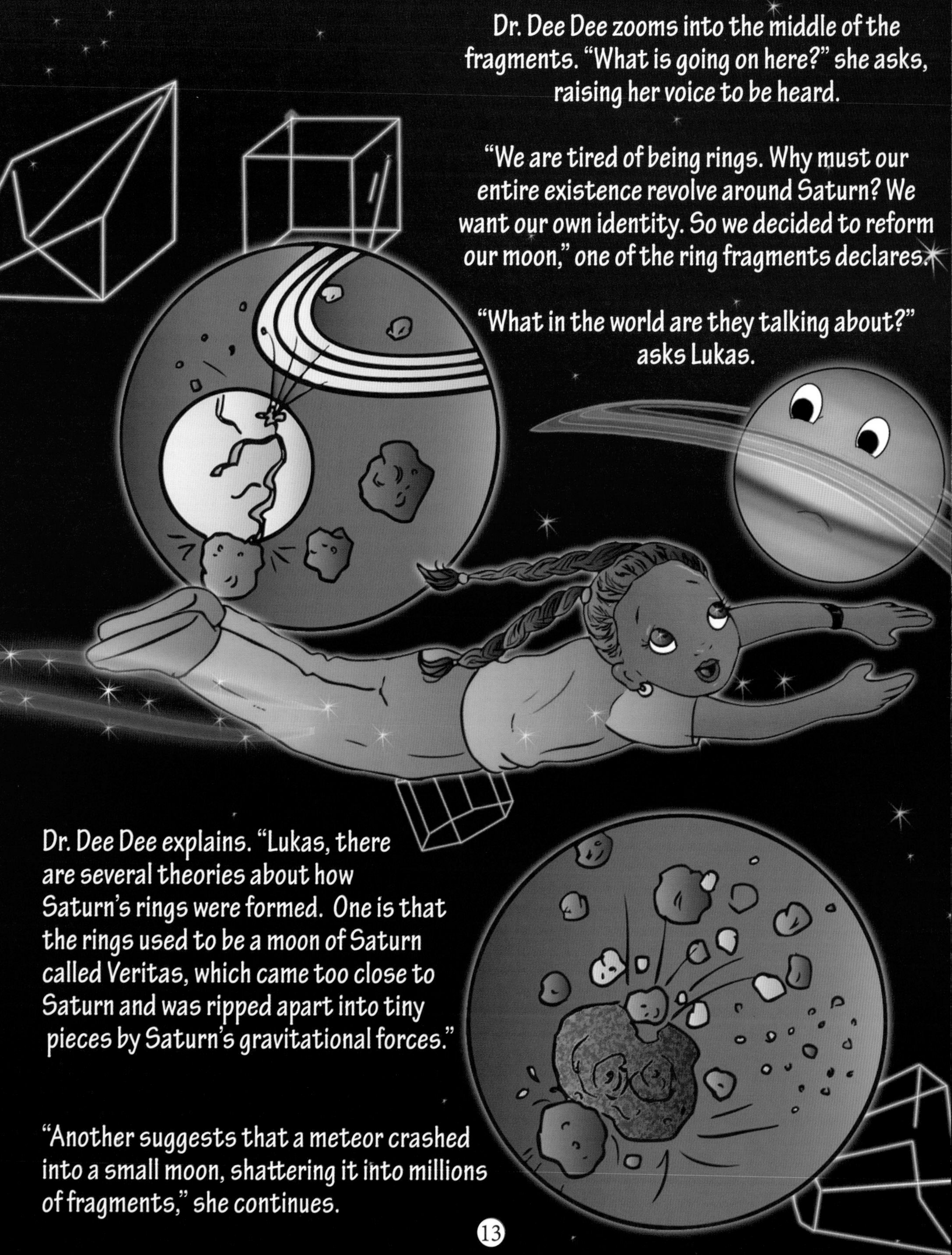

Dr. Dee Dee zooms into the middle of the fragments. "What is going on here?" she asks, raising her voice to be heard.

"We are tired of being rings. Why must our entire existence revolve around Saturn? We want our own identity. So we decided to reform our moon," one of the ring fragments declares.

"What in the world are they talking about?" asks Lukas.

Dr. Dee Dee explains. "Lukas, there are several theories about how Saturn's rings were formed. One is that the rings used to be a moon of Saturn called Veritas, which came too close to Saturn and was ripped apart into tiny pieces by Saturn's gravitational forces."

"Another suggests that a meteor crashed into a small moon, shattering it into millions of fragments," she continues.

"This is very tricky," Dr. Dee Dee says to the fragments.

"We know for sure that it IS possible," insist the fragments. "Just look at Peggy!"

"My Goodness!" exclaims Lukas. "Who on earth is Peggy?"

"PEGGY is a new moon that may have just been formed near A ring," Dr. Dee Dee replies.

"WHATTTTT!!!!! So the fragments are not crazy? Holymackarolee!!!!" exclaims Lukas.

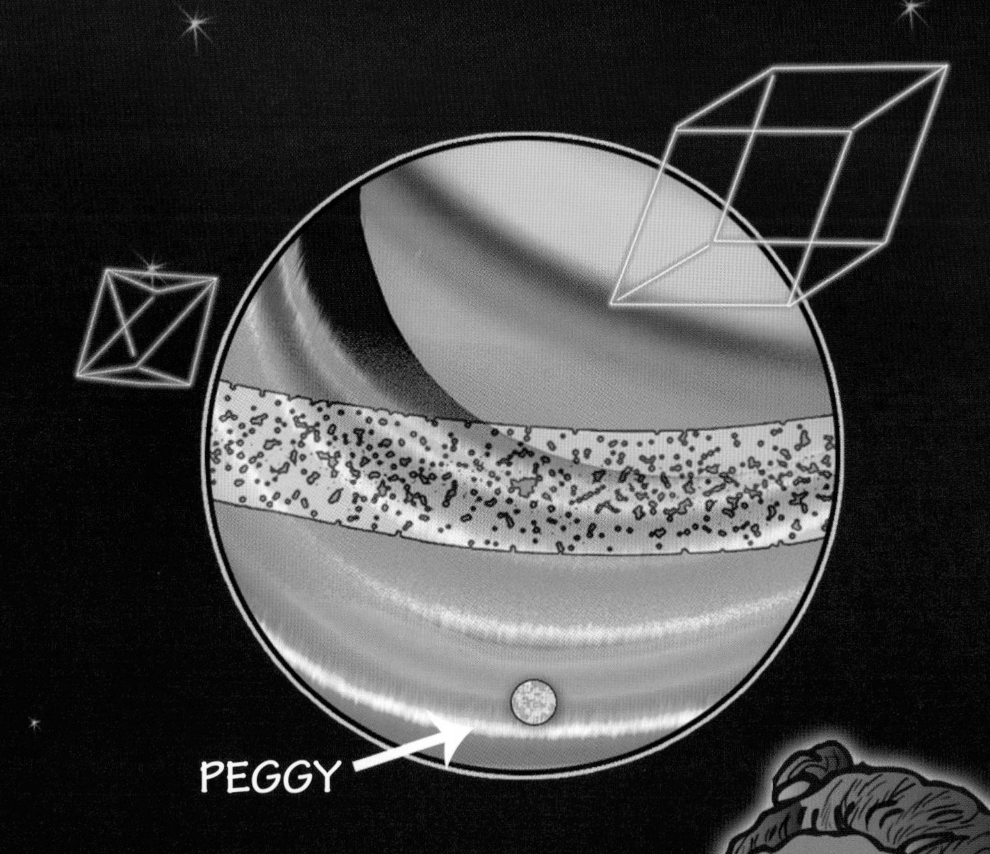

"Even if I were to reconfigure you, there are not enough fragments to create a large moon. You will eventually get sucked back into Saturn's gravitational field and disintegrate all over again," reasons Dr. Dee Dee.

"Uggghhhh, that does not sound very appealing!" a large fragment moans. "We don't seem to have much choice."

SHEPHERD MOONS

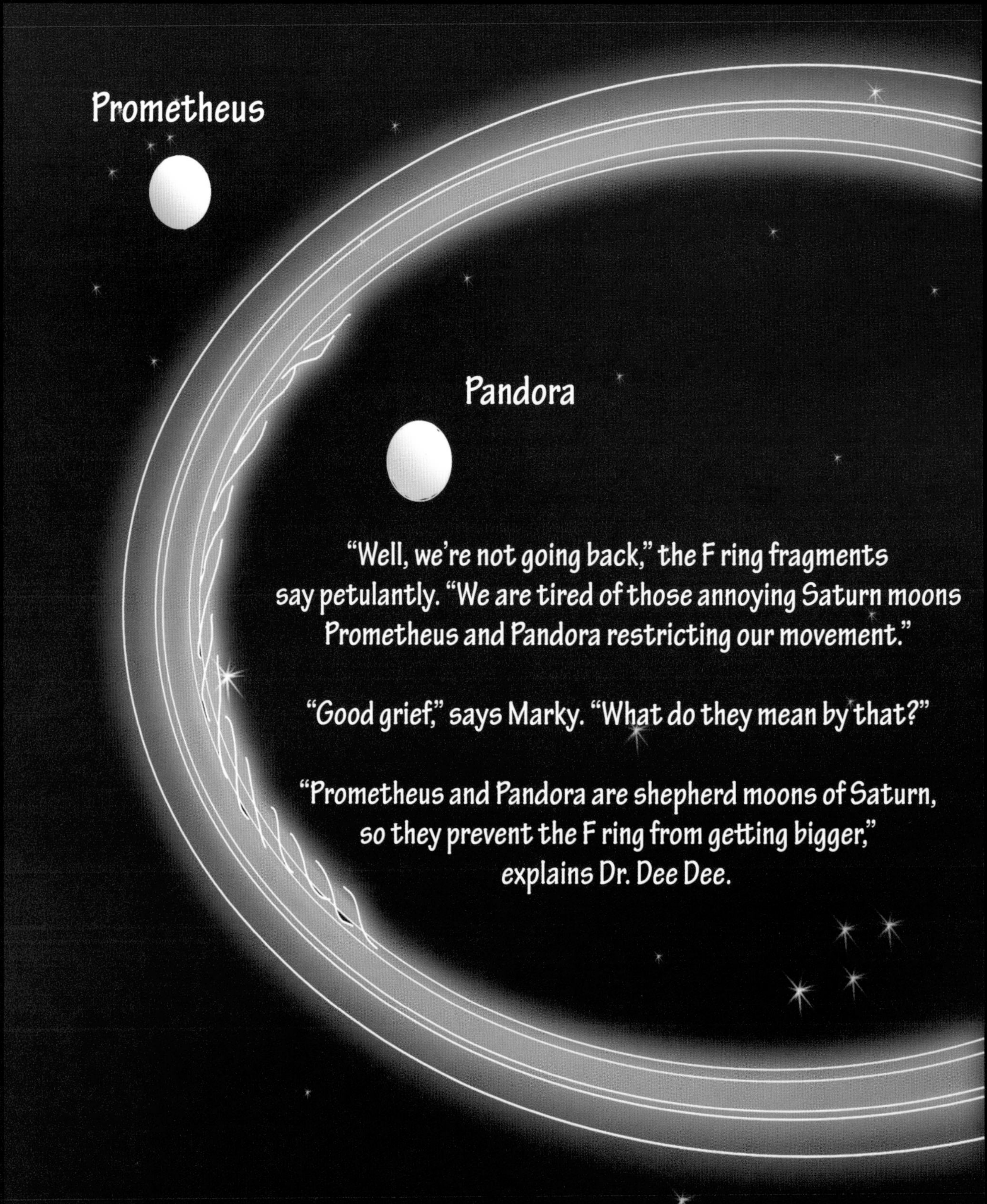

Prometheus

Pandora

"Well, we're not going back," the F ring fragments say petulantly. "We are tired of those annoying Saturn moons Prometheus and Pandora restricting our movement."

"Good grief," says Marky. "What do they mean by that?"

"Prometheus and Pandora are shepherd moons of Saturn, so they prevent the F ring from getting bigger," explains Dr. Dee Dee.

MOONS OF SATURN

First moon discovered was Titan in 1655 by Christiaan Huygens.

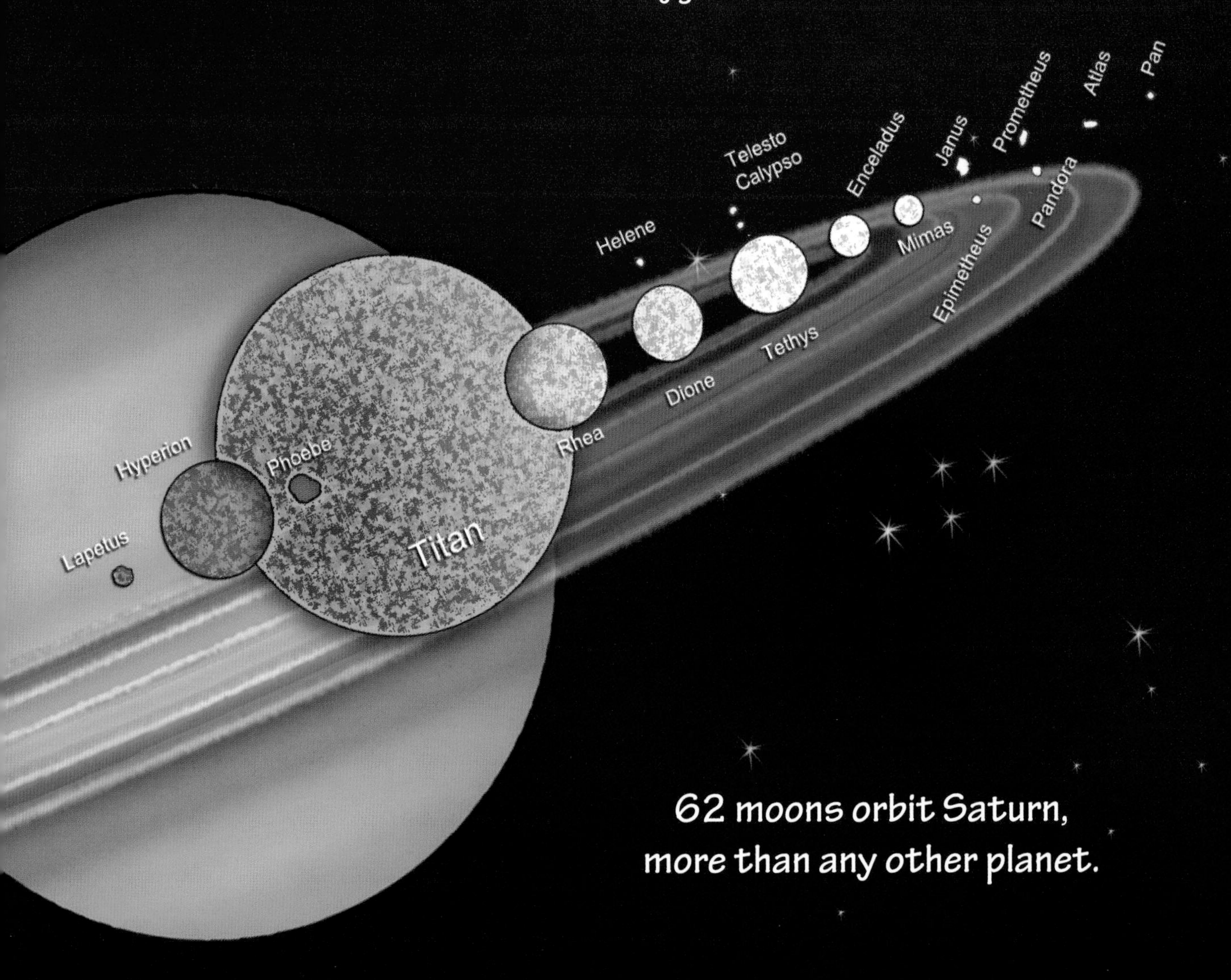

62 moons orbit Saturn, more than any other planet.

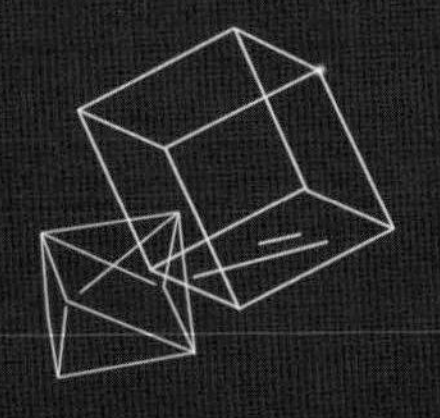

Then, the D ring fragments whisper,
"We'll go back, but can you make our ring a little brighter?"

"Did you hear a voice?" asks Marky. "Where is it coming from?"

"Hmmmmm," says Dr. Dee Dee. "Who's speaking?"

"OVER HERE!" a louder voice says. "We are the D ring fragments and it's difficult for you to see our ring because Saturn and C ring are so bright."

"Whoa, can't miss you now!" says Dr. Dee Dee, turning to the D ring fragments. "I'll see what I can do. However, if you use your voice as you just did, clearly and confidently, no one will overlook you."

"Really, Dr. Dee Dee?" the D ring fragments ask.

"Yes D ring, REALLY!!!" encourages Dr. Dee Dee.

The D ring fragments think about this. "We can live with that," they decide.

Dr. Dee Dee turns her attention back to the F ring fragments.
"We can't do this without you," she says gently.

The fragments huddle. "Okay, Dr. Dee Dee, count us in!"

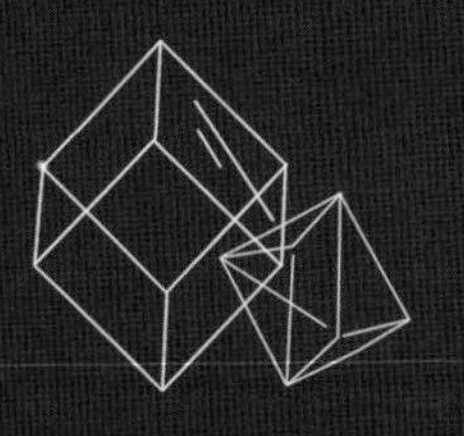

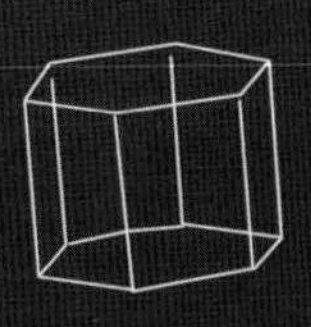

D Ring
C Ring
Cassini Division
Encke Division
F Ring
B Ring
A Ring
G Ring
Use your voice
Be confident
Be assertive

Dr. Dee Dee summons the instruments.
"We have a lot of reconstructing to do."

"How will we know where to put each ring?" Marky asks.

"Just follow me!" says Dr. Dee Dee.

The rings of Saturn go round and round,
Disappeared one day and could not be found.
To put them back, just take a chance,
And join me in the Saturn dance.
The first letter of each move is the name of the ring,
Start closest to Saturn and let's do our thing!

Saturn Dance

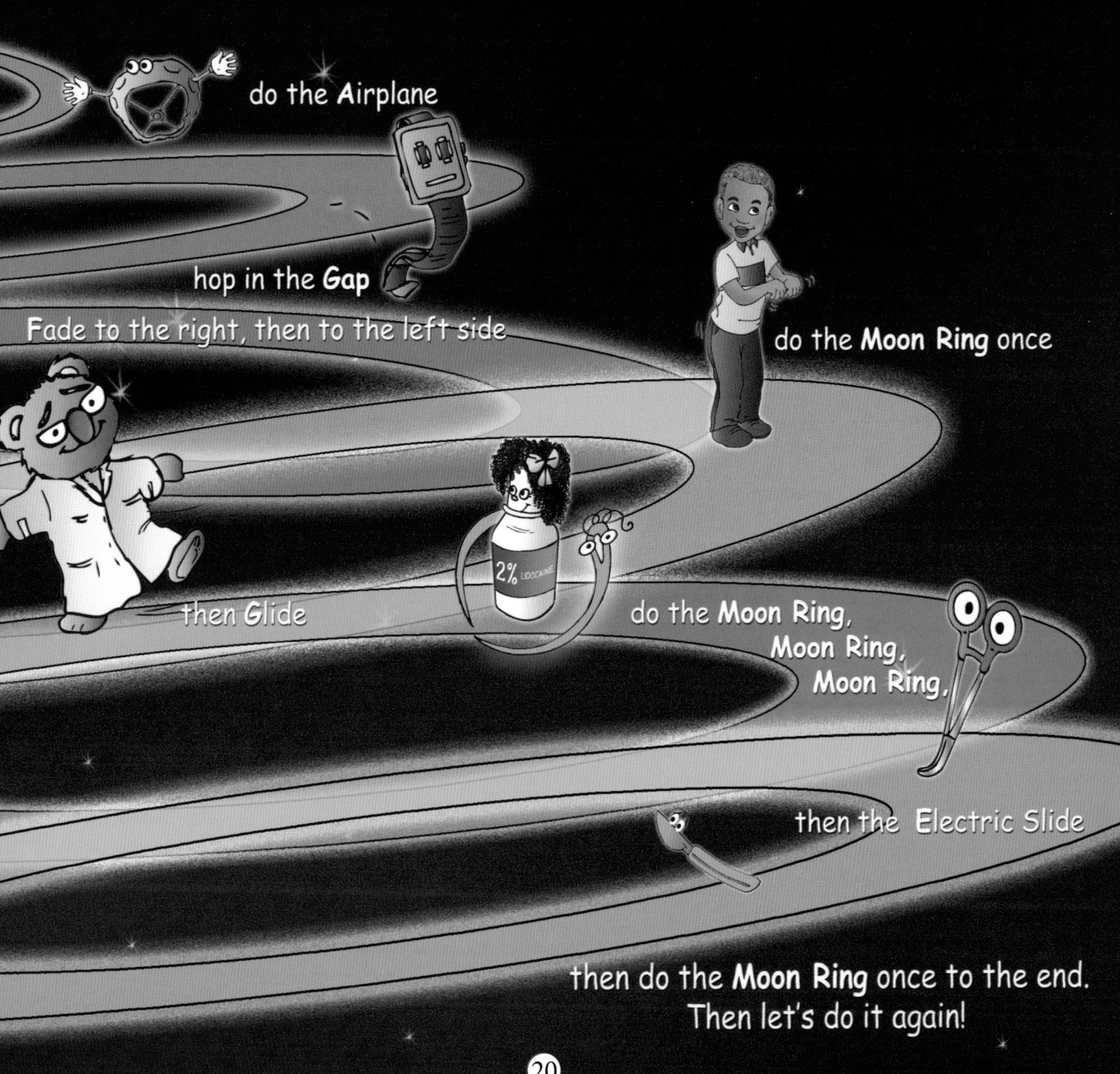

Dr. Dee Dee's fingers are tingling! "Got it?" she asks. Everyone nods.
"Good. Let's get to work, team!"

"I wish I had brought some of my Eucalyptus leaves," Kyle laments.
"This surgery is going to take forever."

"Don't be a pessimist, Kyle," says Lukas. "It won't be that bad."

"Easy for you to say, since you won't be the one assisting Dr. Dee Dee. The rings are 170,000 miles wide, not to mention the circumference around," whines Kyle.

"Holymackarolee, Kyle! Now I understand," says Lukas sympathetically.

The instruments and Kyle zoom out of Freeda and hover alongside Dr. Dee Dee.

They work together until all the rings are reconstructed.

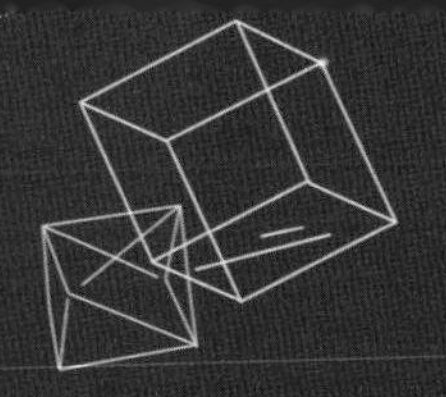

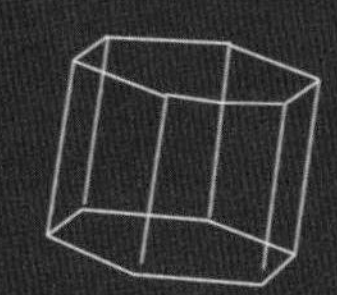

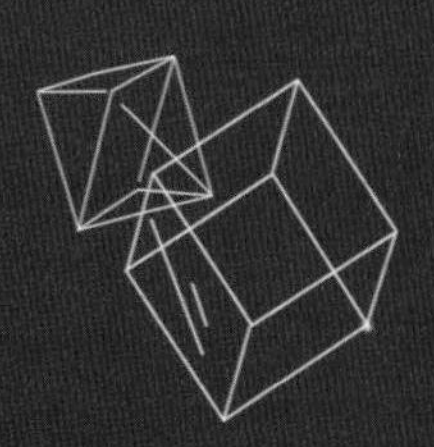

Saturn is *ecstatic*. "Welcome back, rings! I really missed you guys."

Saturn's largest moon, Titan, who has been quietly observing, perks up.

"Dr. Dee Dee, that was amazing," he says. "Can you help me too?"

Dr. Dee Dee looks at Titan quizzically.

Titan gazes at her with woeful eyes and says,
"I would like to have living things on my surface, like Earth."

"That sounds totally unrealistic," comments Kyle.
"Furthermore, what does this have to do with Saturn's rings?"

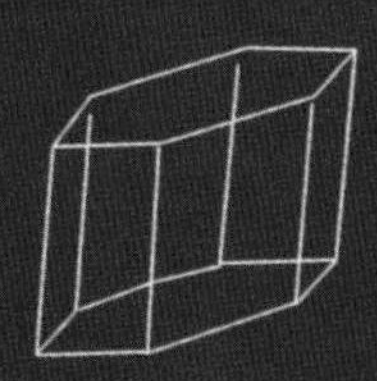

I have liquids on my surface, like Earth.

How a Geyser Forms
Inner core hot rocks heat pressurized underground seawater.
Water vents through cracks in the frozen surface into the very cold atmosphere forming icy particles.
ICE PARTICLES
CRACKS
ICE
SALT WATER UNDER PRESSURE
INNER CORE
HOT ROCKS
CRACKS

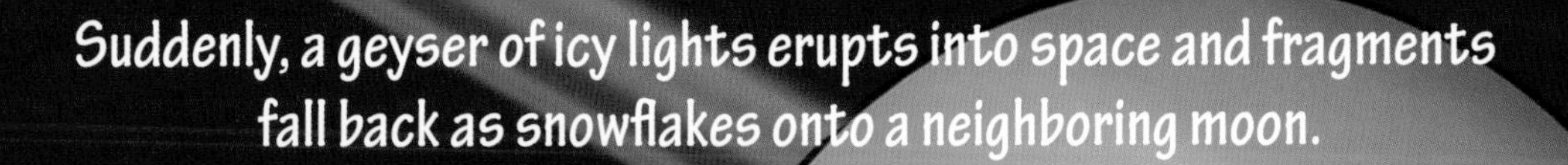

Suddenly, a geyser of icy lights erupts into space and fragments fall back as snowflakes onto a neighboring moon.

"Holymackarolee!" exclaims Lukas.

Kyle is disgusted. "Now what?"

"That's my brother moon, Enceladus, Titan answers, in between sniffs. "He has hundreds of geysers that sprout icy particles, which sometimes escape his gravity and join Saturn's E ring. I think he would prefer to keep his particles to himself. Maybe he wants Dr. Dee Dee Dynamo to help him, too."

Kyle mutters, " Seriously? Does everyone here have a problem?"

"How are we going to figure out if Titan can be like Earth and support life, Dr. Dee Dee?" asks Marky.

"This might be easier than you think, Marky!" says Dr. Dee Dee. "The Cassini spacecraft sent a probe to Titan in 2005 so I bet they can help us."

"A probe? How does that work?" asks Lukas.

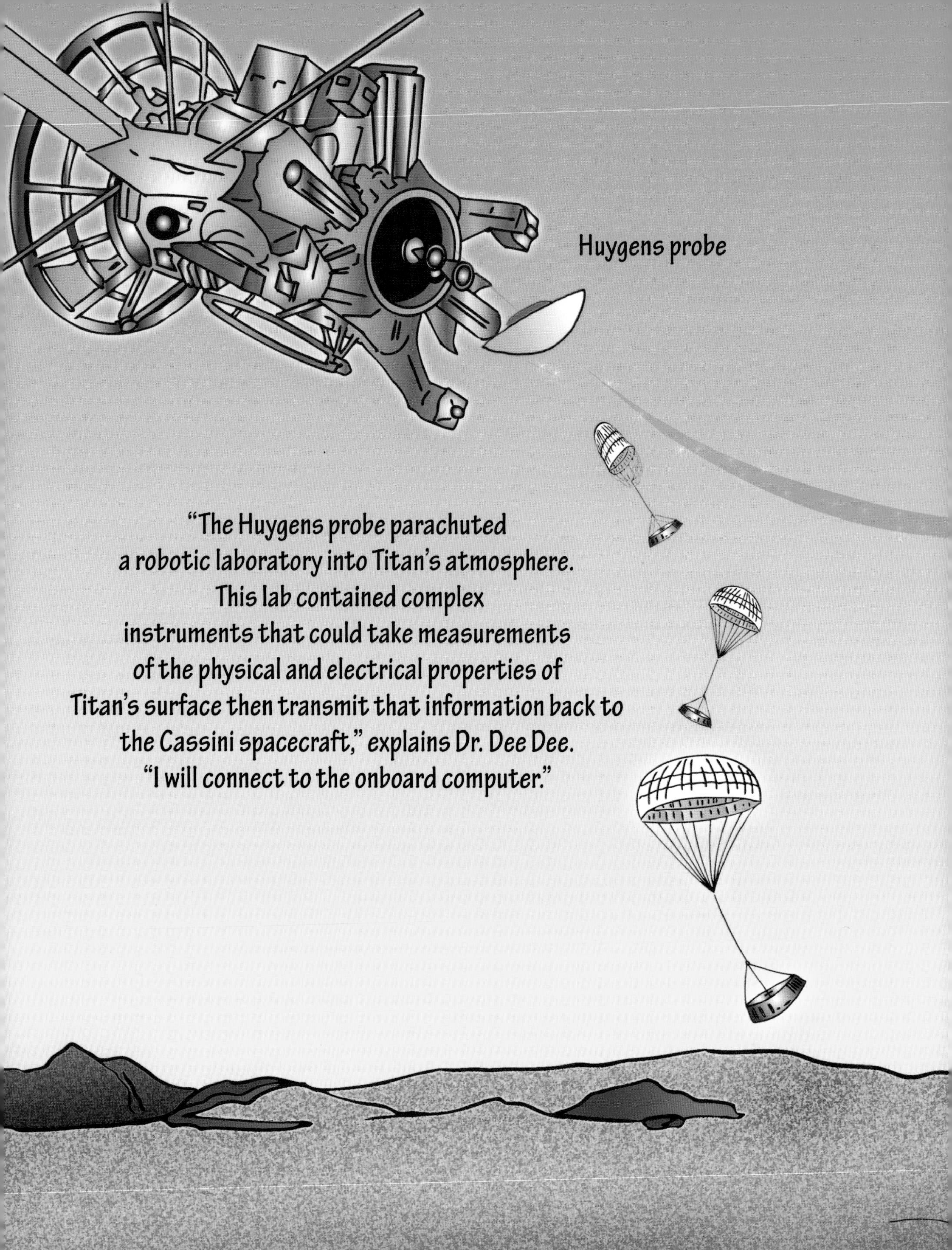

"The Huygens probe parachuted
a robotic laboratory into Titan's atmosphere.
This lab contained complex
instruments that could take measurements
of the physical and electrical properties of
Titan's surface then transmit that information back to
the Cassini spacecraft," explains Dr. Dee Dee.
"I will connect to the onboard computer."

"With your permission of course," she says to Cassini.

"Permission granted," Cassini responds.

Dr. Dee Dee focuses her electrical energy and accesses the Cassini spacecraft computer.

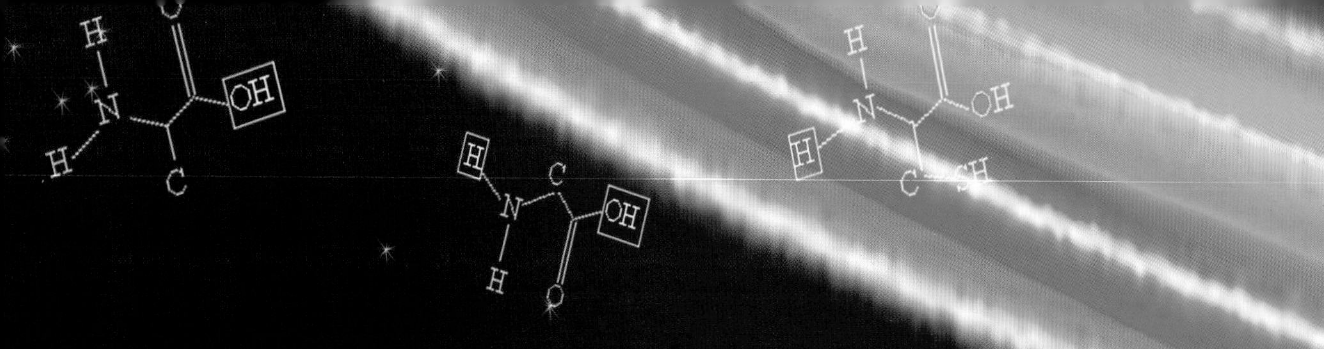

After some time, Dr. Dee Dee faces Titan. "Titan, you have so much potential. Your atmosphere and surface environment are very similar to that of early Earth. Some of your materials are organic and can be building blocks to life. However, this process can take billions of years. Be patient. Earth was probably just like you at one time. And look at Earth now!"

Kyle doubles over with laughter. "Billions of years," he splutters. "Is that supposed to make him feel better?"

"Kyle, please say something encouraging," Dr. Dee Dee admonishes.

"Ummmm... iiiiiin the universe, a billion years is nnnnot that long," Kyle stutters, trying his best to keep a straight face.

Titan listens intently to Dr. Dee Dee.

"Thank you for giving me hope, Dr. Dee Dee," he says.
"I will wait patiently and try not to complain."

"Don't hold your breath," Kyle mutters to himself.

"I heard that, Kyle," scolds Dr. Dee Dee.

"Sorry, Dr. Dee Dee!" says Kyle. "May we go now?"

Dr. Dee Dee addresses Saturn and the rings. "Are you okay?"

"Dr. Dee Dee Dynamo, thank you so much for all your help," says Saturn.
"I now understand how my rings may have felt unimportant.
I felt so incomplete without them so I will make sure that I tell them frequently
how much they mean to me."

"We all feel so much better!" say the rings.
"Thank you for listening and putting us back together."

Saturn and the rings applaud.

"You are so welcome!" beams Dr. Dee Dee.
"I LOVE surprises
and this was definitely a
SURPRISE MISSION!"

"Let's go home, team!
Uncle Beemore is supposed to arrive today with our new beehives."

THE END

GLOSSARY

Cassini-Huygens Spacecraft (kuh·see·nee) – A complex unmanned robotic spacecraft sent to study the planet Saturn. It consists of the Cassini orbiter and the Huygens probe. It left Earth in 1997 and arrived at Saturn in 2004. Named after astronomer Jean-Dominique Cassini who discovered 4 of Saturn's moons in the 1670's.

Enceladus (en·sel·uh·duh·s) - The sixth-largest moon of Saturn, William Herschel discovered it in 1789.

Huygens probe (hahy·guh·nz) - An entry probe designed to study the atmosphere and the surface of Titan (the largest moon of Saturn). Named after scientist Christiaan Huygens who discovered Titan in 1655.

Jupiter's Great Red Spot - A raging red swirling storm located in Jupiter's upper atmosphere. It measures more than 24,800 miles across, 3 times the diameter of Earth. Scientists have been able to see it for over 300 years.

Moons of Saturn - The dozens of icy moons orbiting Saturn. They vary drastically in shape, size, surface age and origin. Some of these worlds have hard, rough surfaces, while others are porous bodies coated in a fine blanket of icy particles.

NASA - National Aeronautics and Space Administration. NASA is in charge of U.S. science and technology that has to do with airplanes or space.

Peggy - A small icy object located near Saturn's A ring believed to possibly be a 'newly born moon.' Photography by Cassini's cameras on April 15, 2013, has recorded what is thought to be first ever documentation of a possible 'moon birth.'

Ring Plane Crossing - Saturn's movement through its orbit occasionally causes its rings to disappear. This occurs when the tilt of the planet and its position in its orbit combine to allow a side-on view of the rings from Earth resulting in seeming disappearance of the rings.

Ringed Planets - Planets that contain a ring of dust, moonlets, or other small objects orbiting a planet. The ringed planets are Jupiter, Neptune, Saturn and Uranus. These are also known as gas planets.

Saturn - 6th planet from the Sun. It is named after the Roman God of Agriculture. It is the 2nd largest planet- 763 Earths can fit inside Saturn. A day on Saturn is 10.5 hours.

Saturn's Rings- Saturn's spectacular ring system has billions of tiny particles of ice and rocks of varying sizes in orbit around the planet. The ring particles range in size from smaller than grains of sugar to as large as a house. They were first observed by Galileo in 1610 and described by Christiaan Huygens in 1655. They measure 170,000 miles across and 65 ft thick.

Shepherd Moons - A moon or satellite that orbits around its planetary neighbor and affects objects on or around the planet. From the influence of gravity and mass, a moon can affect tides, weather and even the paths of orbiting objects.

Titan (tahyt·n) - The largest moon of Saturn, It is the second largest moon in the Solar System. Titan is larger than the planet Mercury.

LEARNING WORDS

Adamant (ad·a·mant) -refusing to be persuaded or to change one's mind.

Commotion (com·mo·tion) - a state of confused and noisy disturbance.

Compassion (com·pas·sion) - sympathetic pity and concern for the sufferings or misfortunes of others.

Dejected (de·ject·ed) - sad and depressed; dispirited.

Disintegrate (dis·in·tuh·greyt) - Break up into small parts, typically as the result of impact or decay.

Ecstatic (ec·stat·ic) - feeling or expressing overwhelming happiness or joyful excitement.

Frazzled (fraz·uh·ld) - Cause to feel completely exhausted; wear out.

Geyser (gahy·zer) - A hot spring in which water intermittently boils, sending a tall column of water and steam into the air.

Hastily (hey·ste·ly) -With excessive speed or urgency; hurriedly.

Hover (huhv·er) - An act of remaining in the air in one place.

Immerse (im·merse) - involve oneself deeply in a particular activity or interest.

Lament (la·ment) - a passionate expression of grief or sorrow.

Pandemonium (pan·de·mo·ni·um) - wild and noisy disorder or confusion; uproar.

Petulant (pet·u·lant) - childishly sulky or bad-tempered.

Quizzically (kwiz·i·kuh·ly) - in a questioning manner.

Reassure (ree.a.shore) - Restore confidence.

Reconfigure (ree·kuh·n·fig·yer) - to rearrange.

Sheepish (sheep·ish) - showing embarrassment.

Simulator (sim·yuh·ley·ter) - A machine with a similar set of controls designed to provide a realistic imitation of the operation of a vehicle or other complex system, used for training purposes.

'Stark raving mad' - Completely crazy.

Touché (tou·ché) - used to admit that someone has made a clever or effective point in an argument.

Unnerving (un·nerve·ing) - make (someone) lose courage or confidence.

Woeful (woh·fuh·l) - expresses grief, misery or sorrow.

Mommy Dynamo's Discovery Questions

1) Saturn's rings were the main reason for Dr Dee Dee's visit.
   a) How many rings does Saturn have?
   b) What are the names of the rings?

2) What are the rings made of?

3) Under what circumstances are Saturn's rings are invisible from Earth? What is this phenomenon called?

4) There are many possible ways in which the rings could have been formed. What are the two causes given in the story for the formation of the rings?

5) In addition to rings, Saturn has many moons. Some of the moons are named in the story.
   a) Write the names of the moons given in the story.
   b) Which of these moons is the largest?

6) Give examples in this story that show how technology has helped scientists to obtain detailed and accurate information about Saturn's rings, moons, movement, and its composition.

7) What is a geyser? Look for examples of other geysers around the world. How are the geysers on the moon Enceladus formed?

8) What reasons are given to support that it is possible for Titan to eventually have life forms like Earth?

9. What is your response to Kyle's question "Does everyone here have a problem?"

10) Make up your own song and dance to remember the rings of Saturn.

Mommy Dynamo's Math Challenge

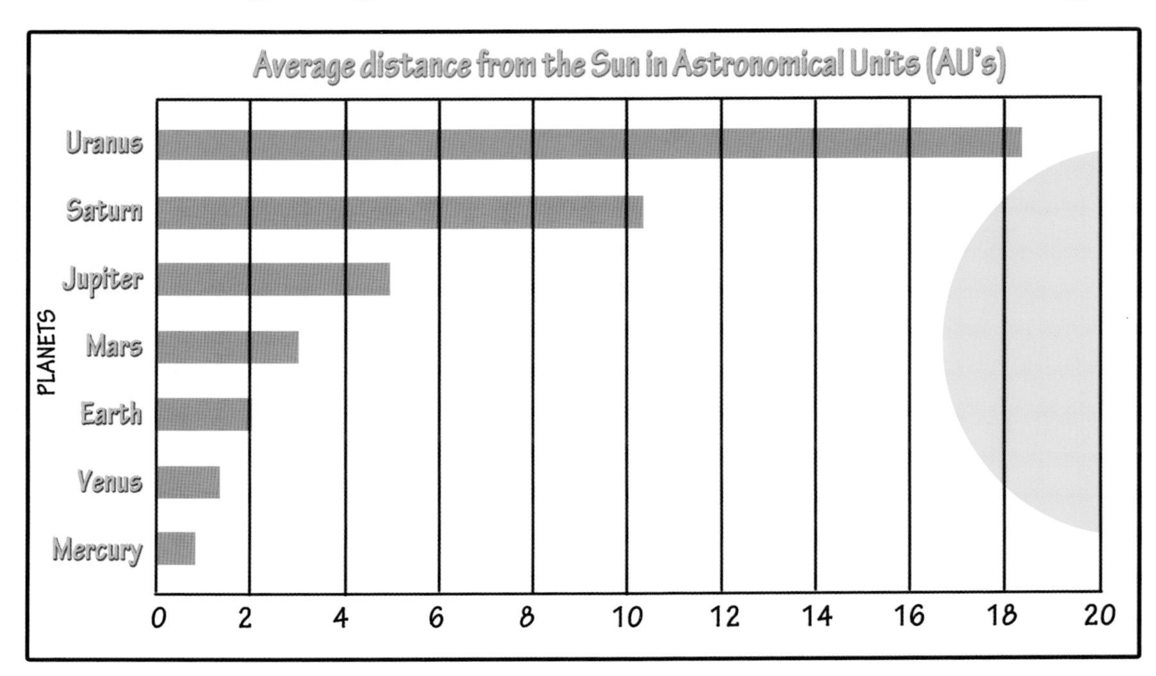

The diagram above shows the approximate distance of planets from the Sun in Astronomical Units (AU) units. 1 AU is equal to 150 million kilometers or 93 million miles.

1. Which planet is missing from the diagram?

2. Name the planets whose orbits Freeda crosses on her way to Uranus.

3. About how many Astronomical Units (AU) did Freeda have to travel to get back from Uranus to Saturn?

4. How far in Astronomical Units is Saturn from Earth?

5. Draw the orbits of the planets around the Sun.

6. Saturn takes 29.5 Earth years to complete one revolution around the Sun. Explain why Saturn takes such a long time to go around the Sun.

7. Using the graph, calculate the distance in miles between
   a) Saturn and the Sun.
   b) Saturn and Earth.

RESOURCE GUIDE

Website Resources

Follow Cassini- Huygens mission at www.saturn.jpl.nasa.gov

Learn more about Saturn at www.solarsystem.nasa.gov

Astronomy for kids at www.kidsastronomy.com

ANSWER KEY

Mommy Dynamo's Discovery Questions

All answers contained within the text and glossary.

Mommy Dynamo's Math Challenge

1. Neptune.

2. Mars, Jupiter, Saturn.

3. Approx 8 AU.

4. Approx 8 AU.

5. Draw the solar system with the planet orbiting around the Sun. www.enchantedlearning.com/subjects/astronomy/planets

6. Because Saturn is approx 5 times farther away from the Sun than Earth.

7. a) 18 AU x 93 million = 1,674 million miles (1.674 billion)
   b) 8 AU x 93 million = 744 million miles (0.7 billion)